BOOK 8
long -i

PHONICS

The Right Surprise

978-1-338-68389-9

10 9 8 7 6 5 4 3 2 1   20 21 22 23 24

Printed in Rawang, Malaysia   106

First Printing, September 2020

Scholastic Inc.

This is Snow White.

She **finds** a cottage.

She looks **inside**.

It is not **tidy**.

She makes the cottage **tidy**.

Now it is **time** for a nap.

She **lies** down.

She closes her **eyes**.

The Dwarfs see a **light**.

What will they **find**?

They **find** Snow White.

What a **surprise**!

The Dwarfs **like** Snow White.

They all **smile**.

It is a **nice surprise**.